LUDWIG VAN BEETHO

(1770 - 1827)

SELECTED WORKS FOR PIANO
Compiled and Edited by Keith Snell

Contents

All pieces in this edition are in original form, with some dynamics, slurs and articulation marks added by the editor as suggestions for musical interpretation. For supplementary study, a recording is available on compact disc (GP378CD) and cassette, performed by pianist Diane Hidy. Ms. Hidy's performance is closely matched to the editorial markings as a practical example for students.

ISBN 0-8497-6193-X

SONATINA IN G

Romanza

Allegretto

* smaller hands:

BAGATELLE IN A MINOR

Opus 119, No. 9

Vivace assai ed un poco sentimentale

* Smaller hands:

SONATINA IN F

I.

8

II. Rondo

*This rolled chord can be played more easily by students in this manner:

SIX VARIATIONS ON A SWISS SONG

Var. II

16

GP378

BAGATELLE IN D

Opus 119, No. 3

18

GP378

FOR ELISE

*) Smaller hands:

MINUET IN G

D. C. al Fine

BAGATELLE IN G MINOR

Opus 119, No. 1

SONATA IN G

Opus 49, No. 2

28

30

Tempo di Menuetto

SIX VARIATIONS
on "Nel cor più non mi sento"
from "La Molinara" by G. Paisiello

Var. II

Var. III

Var. IV *cantabile e doloroso*

Bagatelle in F

Opus 33, No. 3

Six Variations on
an Original Theme in G Major

Theme
Andante, quasi Allegretto

Var. I

Var. II

44

Var. III

Var. VI

SONATA IN G MINOR
Opus 49, No. 1

Rondo
Allegro

54

RONDO IN C

Opus 51, No. 1

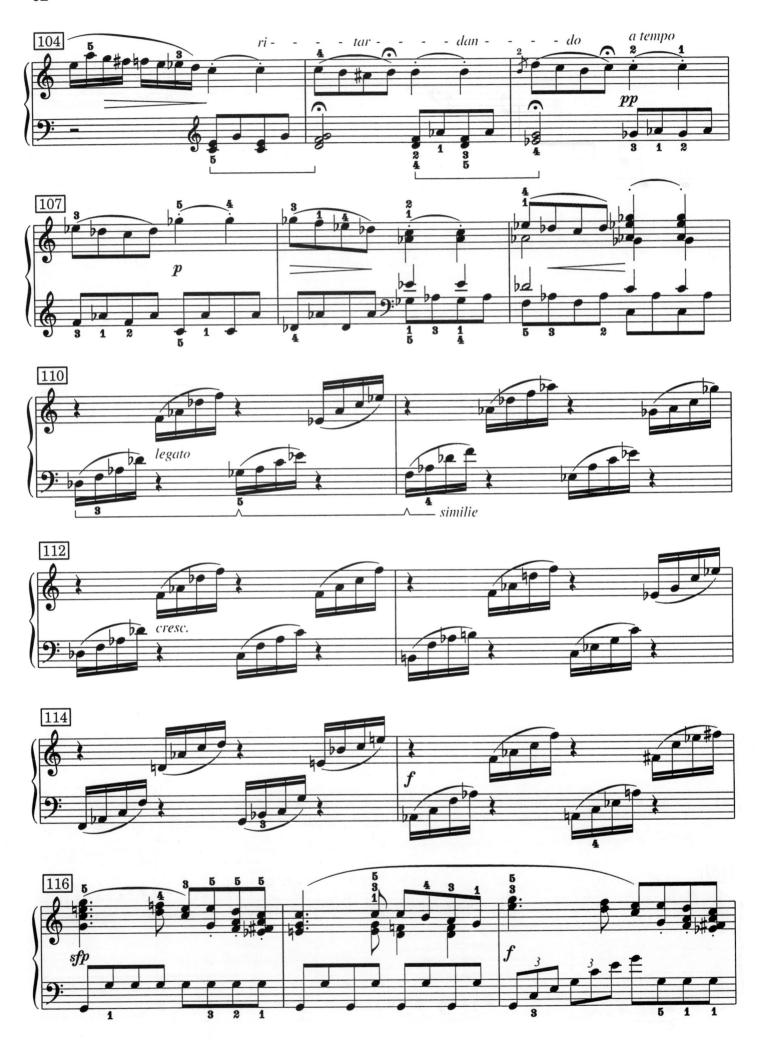

LUDWIG VAN BEETHOVEN
(1770 - 1827)

Beethoven was born in Bonn, Germany in 1770. He received his first music lessons from his father, who was a court singer and instrumentalist. Obsessed with the idea of making Beethoven into a child prodigy like Mozart, his father forced him to practice many long hours.

In 1787, upon the suggestion of his teacher Christian Neefe, Beethoven traveled to Vienna to meet other musicians. It was at this time that he met and played for Mozart. When he later returned to Vienna he studied for a time with Haydn. Both of these great musicians admired his genius.

In 1792, at the age of 22, Beethoven moved to Vienna where he settled for the rest of his life. Here, Beethoven found patrons among the music-loving Viennese aristocracy and began to enjoy great success as a piano virtuoso, playing in private houses or palaces rather than in public.

Beethoven made his public concert debut in 1795, around the same time that his first important pieces were published—the Trios Op. 1 and the Sonatas Op. 2. Beethoven always performed his own compositions with the exception of the two known occasions when he performed a Mozart piano concerto.

1802 was a year of crisis for Beethoven. He realized that the loss of hearing from which he had privately suffered for several years was incurable and was growing worse. That fall, while in a village called Heiligenstadt near Vienna, he wrote a letter to his two brothers describing the anguish and despair he was feeling about going deaf. The tone of the letter suggested that he was considering suicide, but his despair later turned into the strength and determination that lead him into a new creative phase. This new phase is known as his "middle period" of composition. After 1812, Beethoven entered his "late period." During these years he wrote some of his most profound music reflecting the turmoil and spiritual growth of his life.

Beethoven's favorite instrument was the piano. It was for the piano that he found inspiration to write one of the greatest collections of music ever written, the *Thirty-two Piano Sonatas*. Besides sonatas, Beethoven wrote in many other styles—including *variations, bagatelles,* and *rondos*—which demonstrate his supreme mastery of form and structure in music. Beethoven's nine symphonies for orchestra are also among his most beautiful and important compositions.

Beethoven was a well-known public figure by the time of his death in 1827. It is said that over 10,000 people attended his funeral. His grave is located at the Central Cemetery in Vienna, next to the grave of Franz Schubert.

The painting on the cover of this book, *Castle of Bentheim* (1653), is by Dutch landscape painter Jacob van Ruisdael (ca. 1628-1682).